BIG stickers for little hands

MAGICAL UNICORNS

Explore the magical world of unicorns in this sweet activity book!

•

Use pens, pencils and stickers to complete the activities on each page.

•

Where there is a missing sticker, you will see an empty shape. Search your sticker pages to find the missing sticker.

Don't forget to press out and create a pretty puzzle and beautiful bunting from the card pages at the back of the book!

make believe ideas

Unicorn forest

Colour the enchanted forest.

Who is sleeping?
Trace the tick when
you've found the bunny.

Fairy picnic

Finish the fairy picnic.

Trace the cookie.

Sticker the jar of jellybeans.

Doodle tasty toppings on the cupcakes.

3

Wonderful wand

Join the dots to finish the wand.
Then, count to five.

Make a wish!

Odd one out

Circle the one that doesn't belong in each row.

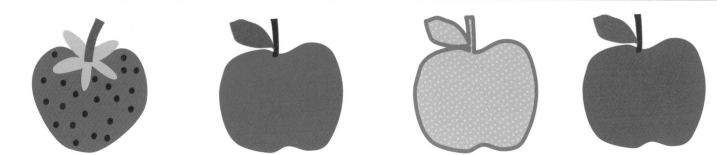

Midnight magic

Colour the magical unicorn.

How many stars
can you count?
Write the answer. ....

Horseshoe havoc!

Draw a line to match each unicorn to the correct coloured horseshoe.

Palace paths

Use a pencil to trace the path to the unicorn palace.

Start here!

How many strawberries can you count?
Write the answer: ....

Flower sums

Count the flowers to finish the sums.

3 + 2 = ...

1 + 3 = ...

2 + 3 = ...

9

Fairy folk

Find three differences between the scenes.

Sticker the star when you have finished and say, "I did it!"

Palace path

Follow the lines to see who is going to the palace.

Unique unicorns

Use colour and stickers to finish the page.
Say the colours as you go!

blue

yellow

red

green

Pamper day

Trace the lines to finish the horn.
Then, colour it in.

Sticker the nail varnish to finish the pattern.

Big top!

Search the circus for the things below.

1 unicorn   2 top hats   3 balloons

Chase the rainbow

Finish the rainbow. Use the coloured dots as a guide.

Picture perfect

Press out the puzzle pieces and mix them up. Then, put the pieces back together to make this picture.

Beautiful bunting

Press out each flag and shade the reverse sides.
Ask an adult to help you fold the tops and tape them
over some ribbon. Now, hang them wherever you want!

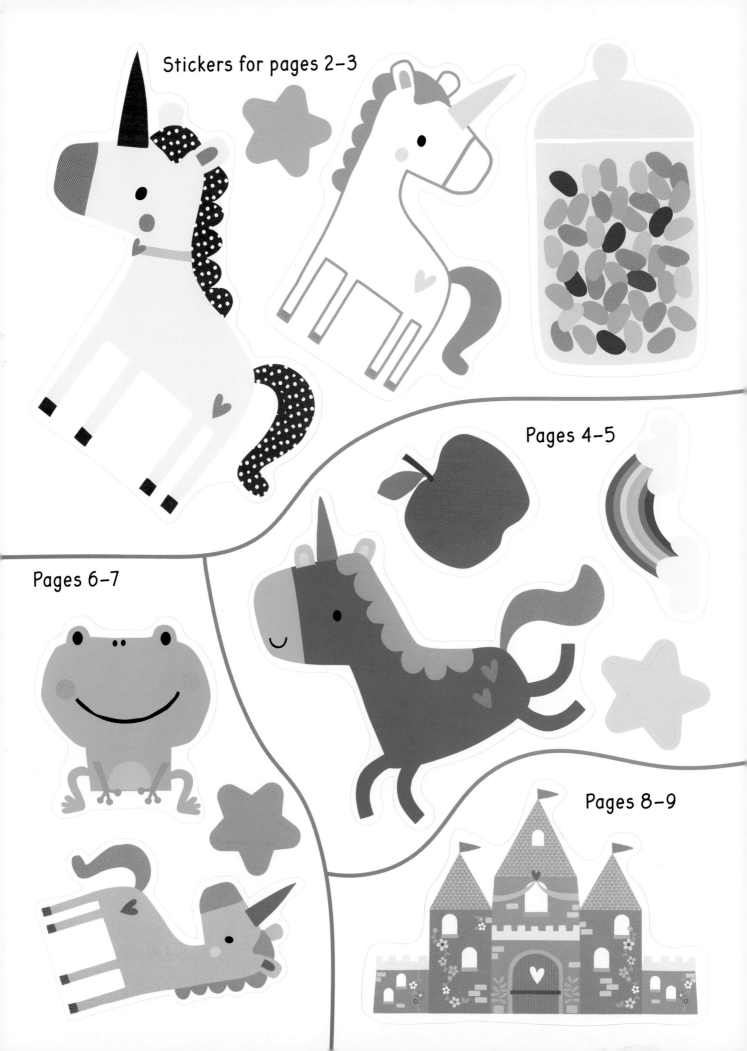

Stickers for pages 2-3

Pages 4-5

Pages 6-7

Pages 8-9

Pages 8–9 continued

Pages 10–11

I did it!

Pages 12–13

Pages 14–15

Page 16

CRAYON